the **BAD GUYS**

in

CUT TO
THE CHASE

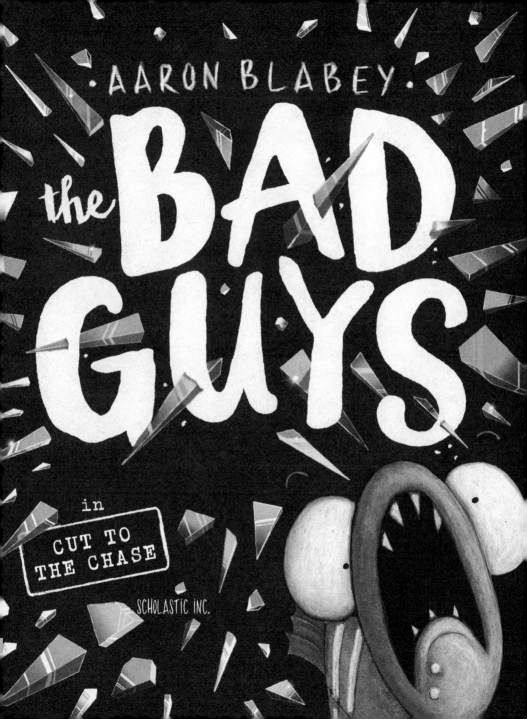

Ugly Snake!

Ugly Snake!

Hey there, little buddy.
Are you OK?

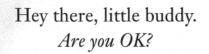

• CHAPTER 1 •
FORGET WHAT YOU KNOW

KITTY!

I can't

slow us

down!

This

isn't

HOT POOP

STORAGE!

I

WANT

HOT POOP

STORAGE!

I really love

you guys!

And

I always

will!

GOOD-BYE!

A realm?! You expecting to see dragons and enchanted snowmen and singing squirrels?

They've got *singing squirrels?!*

Look, all I know is we've just fallen through a **PORTAL** into a place that's not in OUR universe. It's a **WHOLE NEW** dimension, or universe, or realm . . .

CHICAS!
WHAT'S HAPPENING?!
WHERE IS EVERYONE?!

Piranha, calm down . . .

THE SQUIRRELS ARE HERE!

THEY'RE TELLING ME TO
CALM DOWN!

I thought you said they only
communicated through *song* . . .

It's me, you idiot . . . *WOLF!*

Ohhhh . . . I *thought* that was a
deep voice for a squirrel . . .

And now it's day again . . .

That was **NIGHT?!**

It lasted about thirty seconds!

How long do the *days* last?!

And what just hit us?!

Why are we covered in bits of jagged,

pointy hard stuff?!

I don't know.
But this place seems . . .
hostile . . .

And *SHARP!*

Like, sharper than my uncle
Gustavo on a Saturday night.
I mean, seriously, why is
everything here so sharp?!

I don't want to know.

Let's just find the

NEXT DOORWAY

and get out of here.

The *next* doorway?! *We just got here!*

Shouldn't we at least look around for the

EVIL
CENTIPEDE-LOOKING
DUDE for a bit?

I mean, how many doorways do
we have to go through to find him?!

Ooowee!
That never gets old!

He could be
ten more universes
away from here. Fifty more! *A hundred!*
I don't know.
But what I do know, is that he's **NOT HERE.**
So all we can do is find the **NEXT DOORWAY**
and move on to the **NEXT UNIVERSE.**

Wait . . . what?

I've been meaning to ask— **HOW** do you guys keep finding these doorways?

I remember seeing the HOT POOP door, but I don't recall how we got there or why we . . .

Oracle?

GAK!

Oracle . . .
WHERE IS THE DOORWAY TO THE NEXT UNIVERSE?!

THIS WAY!
IT IS
THIS WAY!

Morning, everyone . . .

THIS WAY!
IT IS
THIS WAY!

And away they go . . .

THIS WAY!

· CHAPTER 2 ·
THE VOMIT COMET

VRRRP!

VRRRP!

VRRRP!

VRRRP!

RP!

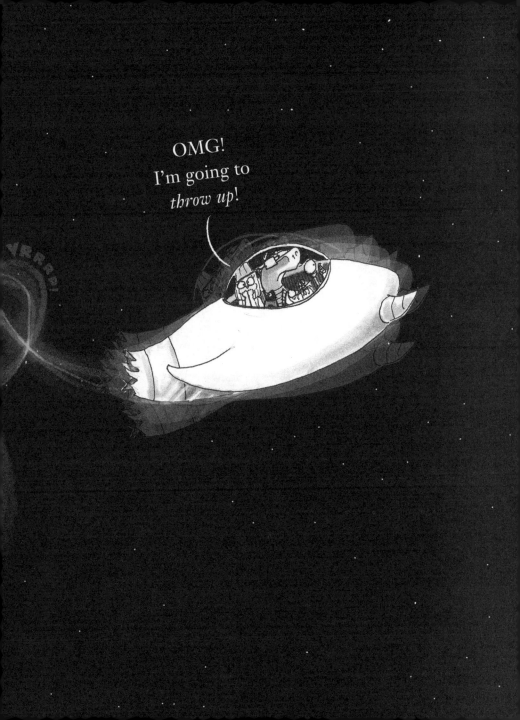

No, you're not, Fluffit.

We've made it

NINETEEN LIGHT-YEARS

across space without anyone throwing up, and the first one to do it is **NOT** going to be **ONE OF US GIRLS!**

Bllurgh . . .

ON THE WRONG TEAM

How far to our destination, Nathan?

How far until we reach **THE OTHERS?**

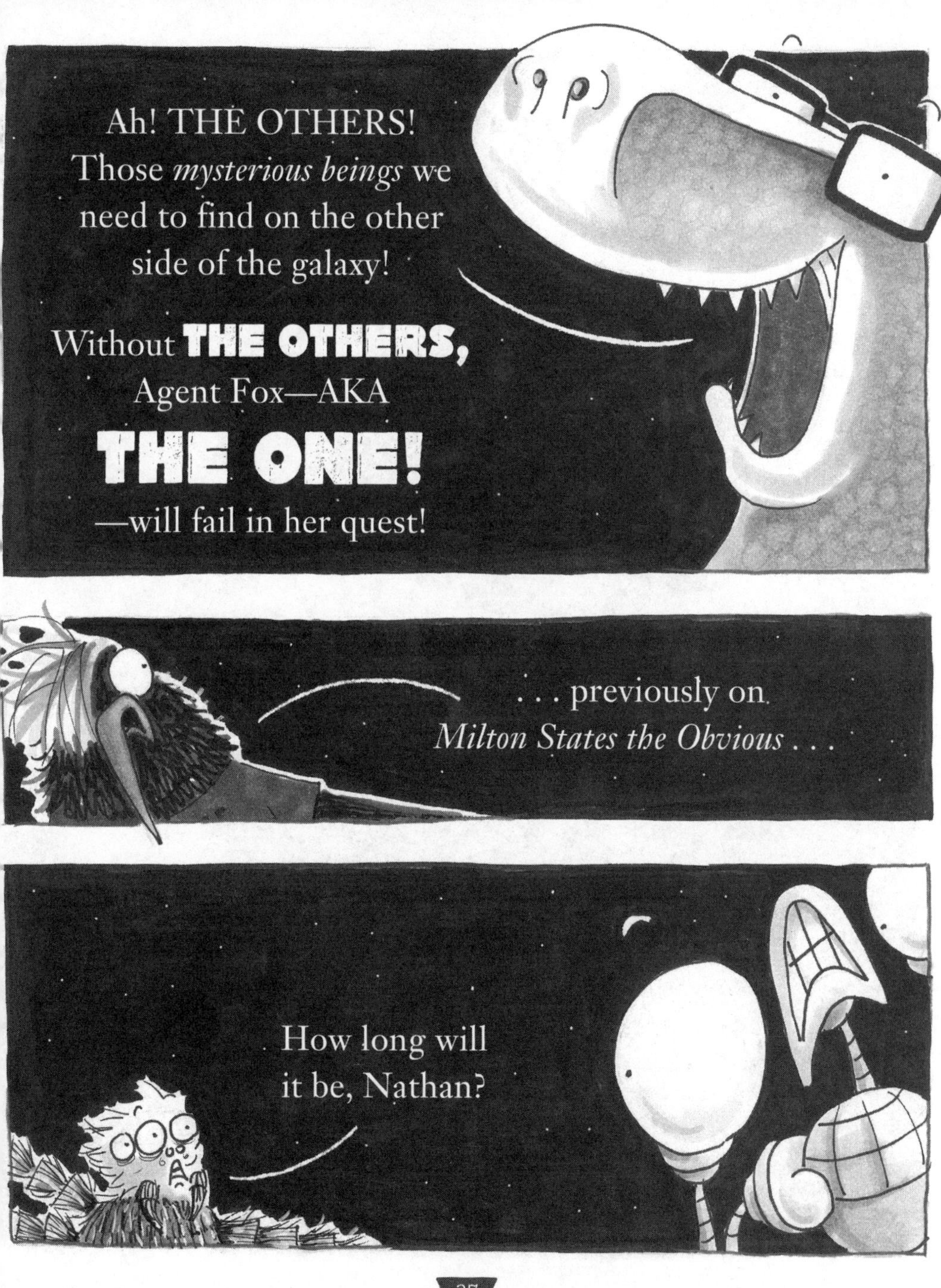

Ah! THE OTHERS! Those *mysterious beings* we need to find on the other side of the galaxy!
Without **THE OTHERS,** Agent Fox—AKA **THE ONE!** —will fail in her quest!
. . . previously on *Milton States the Obvious* . . .
How long will it be, Nathan?

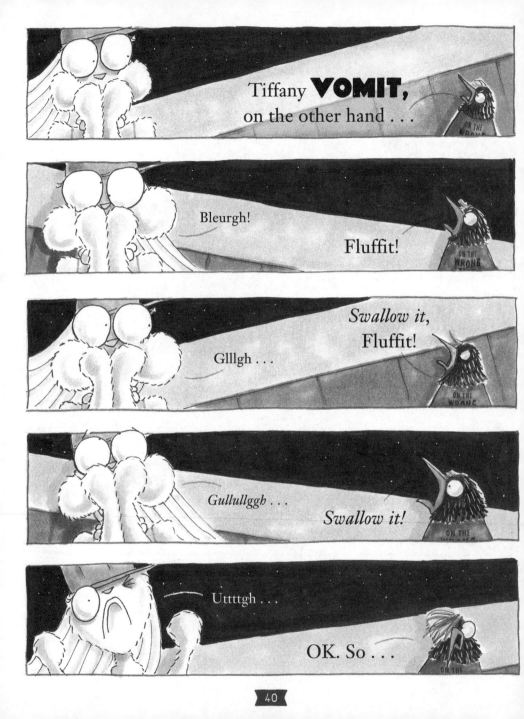

Yeah . . . so, anyway . . .

I was thinking . . . maybe we could

ask my **KING** for a **NEW SHIP?**

One that would get us to

THE OTHERS

a little faster . . .

Your KING?
The father of
MARMALADE?

Uh-huh . . .

You said it!
The one thing we are NOT doing is paying a visit to a **PREVIOUS VILLAIN**.
And I'll tell you why . . .

Ooooh . . . on second thought,
I *do* feel a little funny . . .

PAPA!

PEPE?!

PAPA! CAN YOU HEAR ME?!
YES, PEPE!
What's up with the old fish?
Does anyone else feel like the
BUS TO HEAVEN
is about to arrive?

· CHAPTER 3 ·
FISHY MIND POWERS

MUNCH!
MUNCH!
MUNCH!

Well . . .
good night, everybody.

MUNCH!
MUNCH!
MUNCH!

*AND DON'T YOU
EVER JOKE ABOUT
MY PAPA AGAIN!*

SPLOOF!

58

CHAPTER 4

NATHAN'S WARM WELCOME

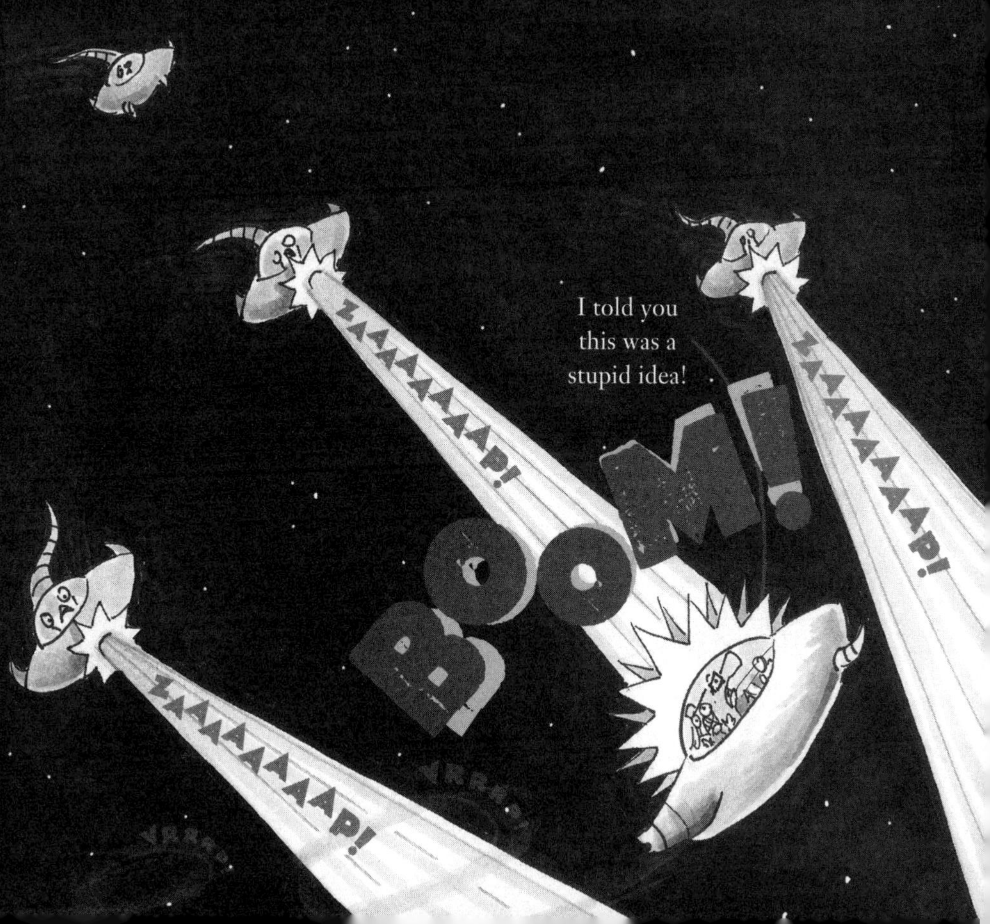

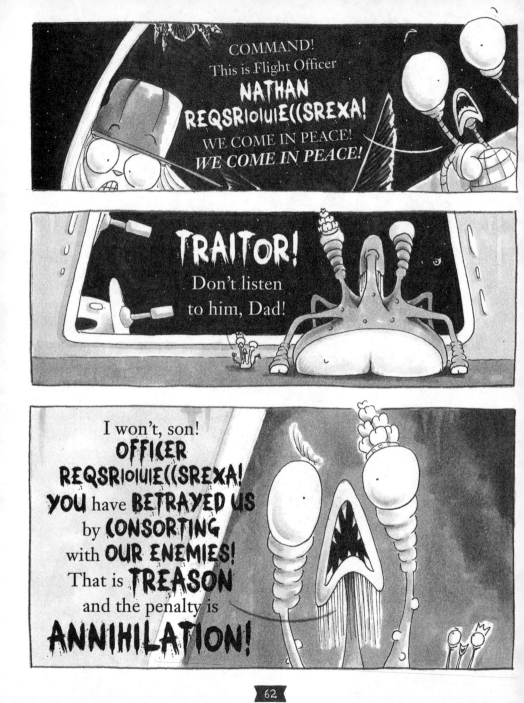

BLOW THEM OUT OF THE SKY!

·Wait!·

The **REAL ENEMY** is on the way! Like a totally evil, end-of-life-as-we-know-it kind of enemy!

And if you don't help us . . .

NONSENSE!
My son told us there was

NO DANGER
of such a thing happening!

Isn't that right, son?

Ah . . . yep . . .

Pretty confident that . . .
yep.

GOOD ENOUGH FOR ME!

You don't mean *THAT* one, do you?!
YOU BETCHA!
GET US DOWN THERE, LICKETY-SPLIT, NATHAN, *MY* BOY!

· CHAPTER 5 ·

DON'T CUT
YOURSELF
ON THAT

So, what's the play?

THAT is the first problem.

It seems to randomly spray shards of glass across the pit every few seconds . . .

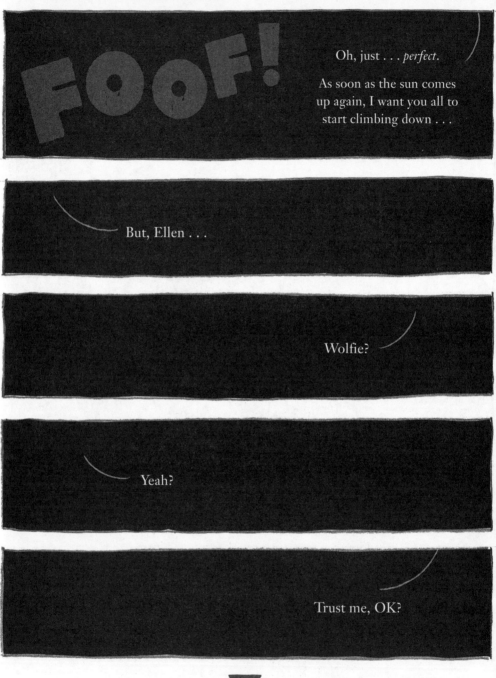

FOOF!

Oh, just . . . *perfect*.

As soon as the sun comes up again, I want you all to start climbing down . . .

But, Ellen . . .

Wolfie?

Yeah?

Trust me, OK?

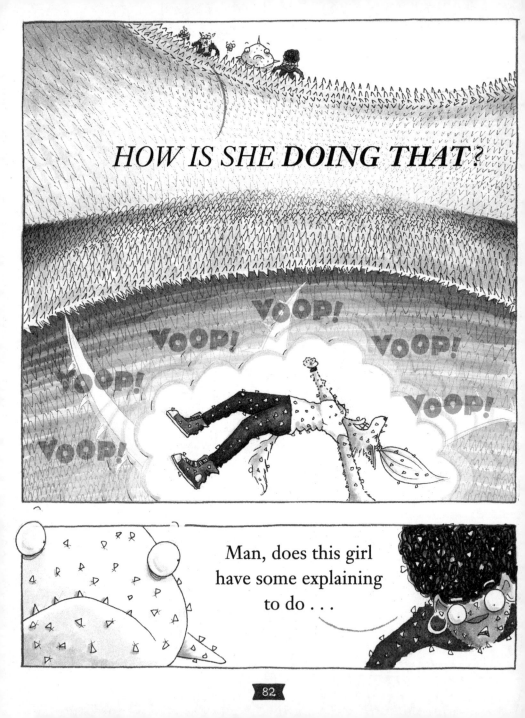

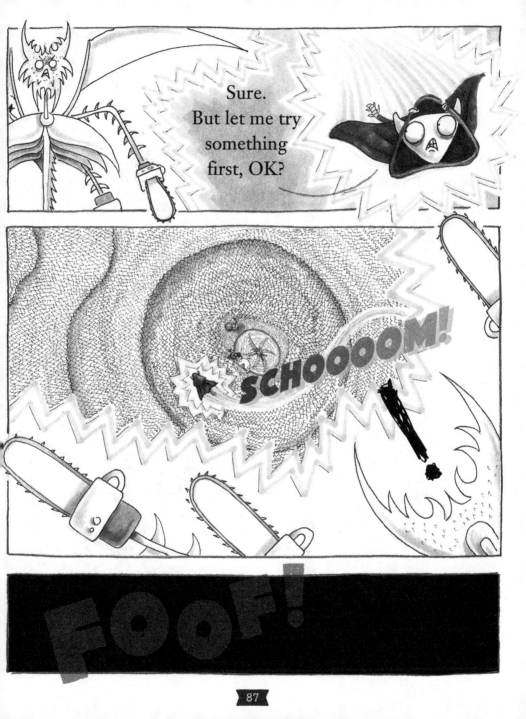

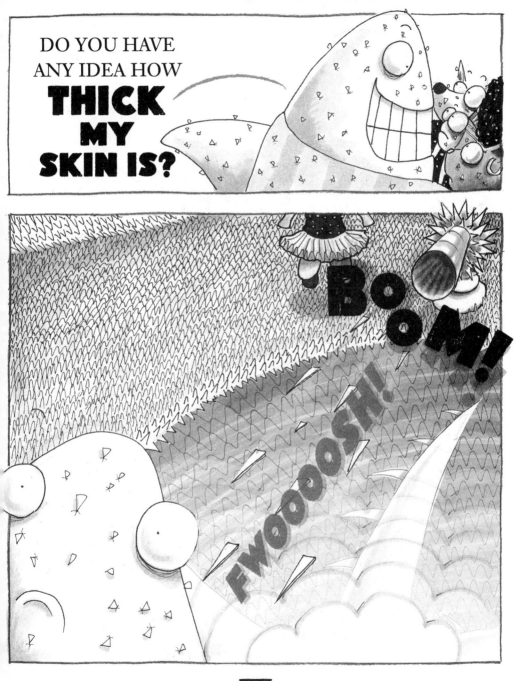

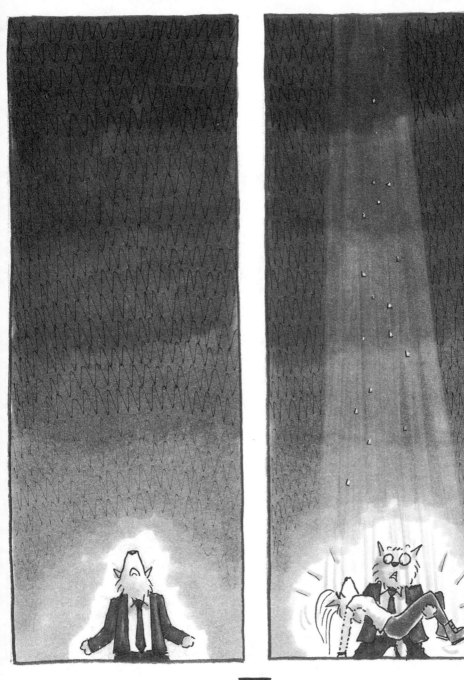

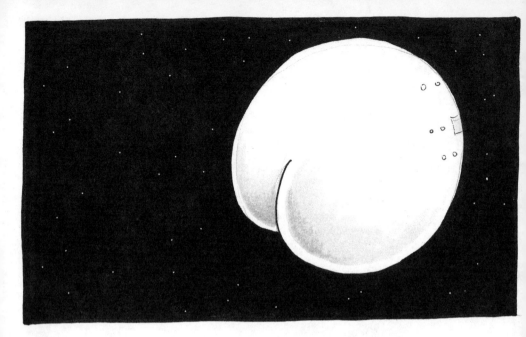

• CHAPTER 6 •
MAKING THE UNIVERSE BEAUTIFUL

It's a big old butt, is what it is.

It's a
GARBAGE FREIGHTER,
actually.

It was designed to resemble a **HAND**—a hand that gathers waste, making the universe beautiful.

It's quite a nice thought, when you think about it that way . . .

SPACE SERVICE STATIONS only come by once every few months.

The chances of one of those flying past us, right now, *exactly when we need it*, are about . . .

FIVE TRILLION *TO ONE* . . .

... 'cause it looks like you guys sure could use some help.

• CHAPTER 7 •
TOO EASY

Heeeey!
It wasn't your fault.
I know it wasn't
YOU.

*Weird.
We're not floating
anymore . . .*

EVERYONE, LISTEN UP!

Emmy, Shark's right—it *wasn't* your fault.

It was **SNAKE.**

But I need you all to understand something—
Snake is getting STRONGER.

He got hold of you, Emmy,
and, for a minute there . . .
I was certain . . .
I couldn't get you back.

This is getting serious,
guys. If he gets any
stronger, I won't be able
to keep him from . . .

FREEZE!

You don't think it's a little

TOO CONVENIENT

that we can all suddenly *walk again*?
Or that the ground is now
magically *safe to walk on*?
That doesn't set off
any alarm bells?

Nope.

· CHAPTER 8 ·
UNBELIEVE-A-BULL

AND EVERY MISSION NEEDS **A LEADER, RIGHT?**

Um . . .

Technically . . .

That's true, but . . .

OMG, *YES!*

THEN, BUTT GUY, **DOES THE SHIP KNOW WHERE TO GO?**

Well, yes. Our destination has been entered into the navigation system . . . but I'd like to make it clear that these really are *hands* and . . .

WELL THEN, LISTEN UP!

• CHAPTER 9 •

VRING NING NING!

May I introduce

UNDERLORD SHAARD.

VRRING!
NING!

NING

Suddenly, butt hands
don't seem so bad . . .

Oh man, here we go again.
Everyone get as
CLOSE TO ME
AS YOU CAN . . .
Urgh . . .
VOOP!
VOOP!
VOOP!
P!
VOOP!
NING!
NING!

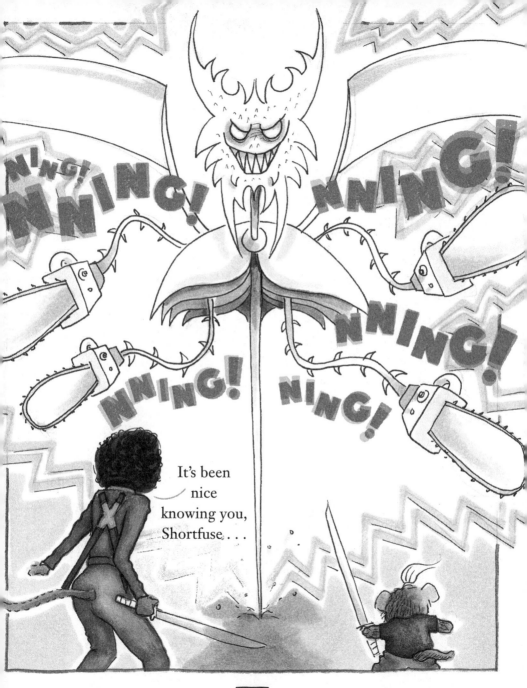

After all we've been through, you really don't know?

Buddy, I'd rather **DIE GOOD** than **LIVE BAD.**

And the Mr. Snake I know would say the same . . .

GRAB!

Ugh . . .

· CHAPTER 10 ·
LONG WAY DOWN

How hard can *that* be?

TO BE
CONTINUED . . .

So, like I told my dad . . .

it's **ALL COOL,** babes.

NOTHING to worry about.

Those Earth guys

are just being

SO DRAMATIC.

They behave as if their life is a

POPULAR SERIES

or something, you know?

And, I mean, EVEN IF their life **WAS**

a series and . . . oh, I don't know, let's say HALF

of them were off in **YET ANOTHER** weird

new universe, looking for an **EVIL CATERPILLAR**

or something, and the other half—let's call them THE B-TEAM—

were off in space with a suspiciously pushy one-eyed bull, looking for some vague but

weirdly intriguing new characters they call **THE OTHERS . . .**

well . . . EVEN THEN . . .

There'd be ABSOLUTELY NO REASON to read th—

the BAD GUYS BOOK **14**!
COMING SOON!